Dear Parents:

Congratulations! Your child is taking the first steps on an exciting journey. The destination? Independent reading!

STEP INTO READING® will help your child get there. The program offers five steps to reading success. Each step includes fun stories and colorful art or photographs. In addition to original fiction and books with favorite characters, there are Step into Reading Non-Fiction Readers, Phonics Readers and Boxed Sets, Sticker Readers, and Comic Readers—a complete literacy program with something to interest every child.

Learning to Read, Step by Step!

Ready to Read   Preschool–Kindergarten
• big type and easy words • rhyme and rhythm • picture clues
For children who know the alphabet and are eager to begin reading.

Reading with Help   Preschool–Grade 1
• basic vocabulary • short sentences • simple stories
For children who recognize familiar words and sound out new words with help.

Reading on Your Own   Grades 1–3
• engaging characters • easy-to-follow plots • popular topics
For children who are ready to read on their own.

Reading Paragraphs   Grades 2–3
• challenging vocabulary • short paragraphs • exciting stories
For newly independent readers who read simple sentences with confidence.

Ready for Chapters   Grades 2–4
• chapters • longer paragraphs • full-color art
For children who want to take the plunge into chapter books but still like colorful pictures.

STEP INTO READING® is designed to give every child a successful reading experience. The grade levels are only guides; children will progress through the steps at their own speed, developing confidence in their reading.

Remember, a lifetime love of reading starts with a single step!

DISNEY · PIXAR

TRACK STARS!

Step 1 and Step 3 Books
A Collection of Three Early Readers

Random House 🏠 New York

Contents

Disney · PIXAR

THE WORLD OF

Cars

Race Team

by Dennis R. Shealy

illustrated by the Disney Storybook Artists

Random House 🏠 New York

Lightning McQueen
is going to a race.

Mack will take him.

All the cars get ready.

Sarge and Flo bring
cans of gas and oil.

Guido loads Fillmore
with water for McQueen.

Guido packs spare tires.

Mater drives in circles.

He is excited!

The cars drive
to the race.
It is far.

Poor Guido gets tired.

Mater gives him a tow.

Big trucks rest
at the truck stop.
The cars keep going.

Mater sees
McQueen and Mack.
There are cars
all around them.

Reporters ask McQueen
about the race.

They take many pictures.

The racetrack is
a busy place!
Mack parks in the pit.

He watches McQueen
practice.

Doc puts on his headset.

It is time for the race.

Mater cheers.

He wants McQueen

to win!

The pit crew is ready.

McQueen drives
to the starting line.
His pit crew yells,
"Go, McQueen, go!"

51 FABULOUS HUDSON HORNET

31

The race starts. <u>Vroom!</u>

McQueen is in front!

He drives the fastest.

McQueen gets tired.

But he keeps going.

Lightning McQueen

wins the race!

Ka-chow!

The race is over.
McQueen and Mack
head home!

DISNEY · PIXAR

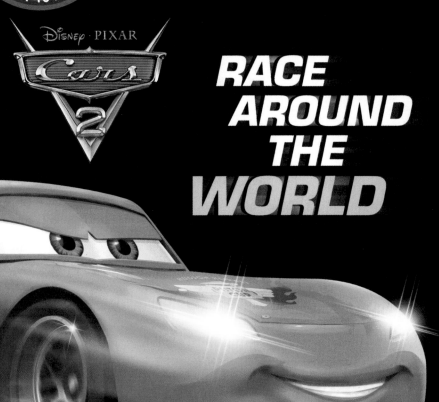

RACE AROUND THE WORLD

by Susan Amerikaner

illustrated by the Disney Storybook Artists

Random House 🏠 New York

Lightning is a race car.

He is fast!

Lightning is a big star.

A car from Italy
is fast, too.

Who is faster?

The cars will race!

The first race is
in Japan.

The car from Italy
is the winner.

Lightning is not happy.

The second race is
in Italy.

Both cars want
to win!

One car spins
on the track!

Lightning wins!

The third race is
in Radiator Springs.
It is the last race.

The cars line up.

The fans are ready.

The cars race!

The fans cheer.

Go, Lightning, go!

Who will win?

by Liz Marsham

illustrated by the Disney Storybook Art Team

Random House 🏠 New York

A new racing season
is here!
Lightning McQueen
takes the lead.
His friends race hard.
They have fun, too.

Jackson Storm
is a new racer.
Lightning tries
to beat him.
Storm is too fast.
Lightning crashes!

Lightning watches a video

of his crew chief,

Doc Hudson.

Doc had a bad crash

and never raced again.

Lightning does not want

to stop racing.

A business car named Sterling

builds Lightning

a new training center.

Lightning is excited!

He is ready

to start training and racing.

Cruz Ramirez

is Lightning's new trainer.

She will use the best

training system

to make Lightning faster.

But the training system

is hard to use.

Lightning breaks it.

Lightning wants
to train his own way.
He takes Cruz
to the beach.

Cruz sinks

into the sand.

Lightning teaches her how

to race on the beach.

Lightning and Cruz
enter a small race.

They wear disguises.

They do not know the race

is the Thunder Hollow Crazy Eight!

Cars crash into each other.

A school bus named

Miss Fritter chases Cruz.

Lightning and Cruz want

to leave the race!

Lightning says

Cruz is not a real racer.

Cruz is sad.

She wants to leave.

Cruz has always wanted
to be a racer.
Lightning feels bad.
He takes her to
Doc Hudson's track.

Lightning and Cruz

meet some famous cars

who used to race with Doc.

They tell stories about him.

He once flipped

over another racer!

Lightning and Cruz train

with Doc's friends.

They pull heavy trailers.

Every day, they get

faster and stronger.

They have a lot of fun, too.

At the end of their training,

Cruz beats Lightning in a race.

She is faster!

Now it is time

for the big race in Florida.

Lightning is nervous.

Finally, the race begins!

Lightning thinks about Cruz.

Cruz did all the training,

just like Lightning.

Cruz is a great racer.

She just needs a chance.

Lightning goes to the pit.

He has an idea.

Cruz will finish the race!

Ramone paints Cruz.

Lightning will help her.

Cruz feels

excited and nervous.

She joins the race!

Cruz catches up to Storm.

Storm is a bad sport.

He pushes Cruz

into the wall.

Cruz remembers
one of Doc's tricks.
She flips over Storm
and wins the race!

Afterward,

Cruz quits her job

as a trainer.

Everyone is shocked!

Tex Dinoco will sponsor her.

She will be a racer!

Lightning will be

her crew chief.

Cruz and Lightning
get new paint jobs.
Lightning is happy
to race with his friend!